D0281592

# Sleeping Beauty

**Phonics Consultant** Susan Purcell

**Illustrator** Rosie Butcher

**Concept** Fran Bromage

Miles Kelly

Once upon a time, a baby girl was born to a king and queen. She was a beautiful child.

**Say** the words as you spot each thing beginning with b in the picture.

baby

bow

bell

2

The king beamed with happiness
and began planning a big party
to celebrate the birth.

**Sound out** these words beginning with the b sound.

**band**   **bird**   **belt**   **bag**
**beach**   **bowl**   **bump**

3

Highlight the ks blend (as in fox) as you read

Excited visitors brought presents in colourful boxes.

The fairies were all invited too, except one, who was extra mean and spiteful.

Can you **see** six presents in the room?

**Spot** the word that doesn't use the ks blend.

fox     mix     ever     wax     exit

When it was time, the fairies waved their wands and cast wonderful spells.

We wish you well!

**Say** the words as you spot each thing beginning with w in the picture.

woman

wand

wings

5

Just as the last sparkly spell was cast, there was a whoosh, and the spiteful fairy spun into the room!

**Sound out** these words with the sp blend.

spark    sport    spider    spent

space    spoon    speak

6

"This will spoil your fun!" she laughed.

"The princess is special indeed! One day she will prick her finger on a spindle and fall down dead!"

**Spot** the word that doesn't begin with the **sp** blend.

sped     spot     spill     sty     spin

How cunning the mean fairy was! The queen collapsed into the king's arms.

"I cannot undo the curse," said a kind fairy. "The princess will prick her finger, but she will just fall asleep. Only a prince can wake her with a kiss."

**Say** the words as you spot each thing beginning with the k sound in the picture.

candle

curl

king

The king immediately called for all the spindles in the country to be destroyed.

**Sound out** some more words with the k sound.

card     coat     keep     kind

bucket     kick     shock     back

Many years later, the princess was exploring the castle, when she saw a door she had not seen before.

**Sound out** these words, which all have the or sound.

born    fork    paw    claw
floor    more    score

Steps led to another door, so the princess thought she would see where it led.

Her father had warned her about wandering off, but of course the princess didn't listen.

**Spot** the word that doesn't use the **or** sound.

warm     brought     room     saw

The princess walked up the steps into a spooky room.

An old woman was sitting on a stool. "What are you doing?" asked the princess.

**Sound out** these words with the oo sound.

moon    boot    do    too

grew    chew    blue    true

"Watch, my child," said the old woman. "I'm spinning – it's such fun. Why don't I teach you?"

The princess stepped forward to touch the spindle.

**Spot** the word that doesn't use the **ch** sound.

chat     bath     peach     match

As soon as she touched the spindle's needle, the princess fell into a deep, enchanted sleep.

"Time to flee!" said the old woman, who was really the mean fairy.

**Sound out** these words with the ee sound.

me    be    tea    clean    seat

sweet    feet    tree

The king and queen also fell asleep. Servants stopped cleaning and dozed off.

Even the pony fell asleep on his feet and the birds stopped tweeting!

Spot the word that doesn't use the ee sound.

meat     slip     green     sheet

Highlight
the ear sound
(as in rear)

Years and years went by and a huge hedge of thorns began to appear around the castle, so no one could get near it.

**Spot** the word that doesn't use the **ear** sound.

clear     dear     where     hear

One hundred years later, a handsome prince was hunting on his horse, when he happened to see the turrets of the castle above the hedge.

Point to some things in the picture that begin with h.

Emphasize the h sound as you say this sentence together.

"What is hidden behind here?"

"Yoo-hoo!" yelled the prince as he hacked through the hedge.

It seemed to take years, yet he kept going.

"You are all so quiet," said the prince when he saw the young servants. "Oh, you're all asleep!"

**Sound out** these words, which all have the y sound.

yes    yelp    yard    yolk
yellow    your    yo-yo

Then the prince remembered the tale of a terrible curse, so he set off to find the sleeping princess.

It was love at first sight as he kissed her. She opened her eyes straight away.

Point out the t sound (as in tale)

Are you all right?

**Spot** the word that doesn't use the t sound.

top     tall     tiny     boat     feel

As the prince and princess crept through the crumbling castle, they brought everyone back to life.

**Say** the names of the things with the br, cr and pr blends, as you spot them.

brick      crown      prince      princess

The princess proudly presented the brave prince to her parents. The cruel fairy's spell had been broken forever!

**Spot** the word that doesn't begin with the **br**, **cr** or **pr** blends.

bring      crab      chip      pram

Sleeping Beauty and the prince were so happy to be together, they were soon married.

They lived happily ever after, and the mean fairy never bothered them again.

**Sound out** the words thin and they. Can you hear the difference?

**Sound out** these words with the hard th sound.

those     there     mother     brother

22

Ask your child to **retell** the story using
these key sounds and story images.

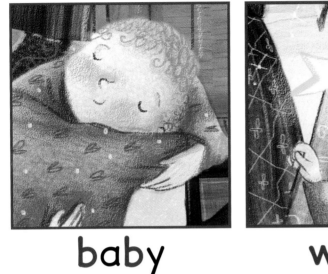

baby

wand

spiteful

king

door

touch

sleep

handsome

together

Say the words in each line out loud together.
Can you think of another word that uses the highlighted sound?

wax    mix    exit    box    six

stool    grew    blue    room

green    seat    clean    sleep

dear    hear    year    near

yard    yo-yo    you    yell    yes

tiny    set    top    feet    tale

brick    broken    bring    brown

crab    crown    cruel    cross

princess    pram    proudly    present

You've had fun with phonics! Well done.

24